The Golden Key Spelling Rules !

By Joan Walton

Spelling Rules and Copymasters

Publisher
Golden Key Publications
28 Mandeville Road Hertford Hertfordshire SG13 8J

Published in U.K. 1994

CONTENTS

PART 1

AUTHOR'S NOTES........... 1

HOW TO USE THIS BOOK... 3

PART ONE- SPELLING RULES

RULES 1- 3...................... 7
Alphabet, Vowels, Syllables

RULES 4-5...................... 15
Word Roots, Doubling

RULES 6-10...................... 21
Magic 'e', Suffixing

Rules 11-15...................... 33
ck or ke, lk/nk/sk, c, k, ic

RULES 16-18...................... 45
Short vowel endings

RULE 19-21...................... 53
Words ending in 'le'

RULES 22-23...................... 61
ly, all, full, till

RULES 24-25...................... 67
'shun', 'shal', 'shus'

RULES 26-28...................... 73
Final 'y'

RULES 29-32...................... 81
Soft 'c', Soft 'g'

RULE 33...................... 91
'w' rules.

RULE 34-35...................... 95
Plurals

PART 2

ai............... 104

ay............... 106

air/are......... 108

ight........... 110

oo/ue/ew........ 112

oi/oy........... 114

o-e/oa/ow....... 116

ou/ow........... 118

er/ir/ur........ 120

or/aw/au........ 122

ee/ea/ie........ 124

cei............. 126

eer/ear/ere/ier. 128

ear (er)........ 130

ough........... 132

el............. 134

Key words....... 136

Silent letters.. 138

Mnemonics....... 140

Golden Key...... 142

Golden Key...... 143
Word List

Index.......... 144

Published in the United Kingdom 1994
First Edition 1994
by Golden Key Publications

Registered at Stationers` Hall
Registration No B9/1181

ISBN 1-874757-09-7

Published by Golden Key Publications
28 Mandeville Road,
Hertford, Hertfordshire SG13 8JG

AUTHOR'S NOTES

"I can read, but I can't spell."

"I've always been a hopeless speller."

How many times do we hear these familiar words spoken by children and adults of all ages? How is it that some people are able to spell correctly with such ease, while others find it so difficult? Weaknesses in sequencing skills or visual discrimination may be contributory factors. Problems vary from person to person. However, I have found that pupils with a wide variety of problems all tend to make the same kind of spelling mistakes.

Some examples are:-

1.   The inability to spell high frequency words which have unusual letter patterns.
2.   The spelling of **vere** for **very**
3.   The spelling of **cind** for **kind**
4.   The spelling of **werk** for **work**
5.   The spelling of **crys** for **cries**

All these errors and many more could be easily avoided by the application of simple spelling principles. After all, about seventy five per cent of the words in our language do follow regular spelling rules.

Spelling rules have been somewhat neglected over the past few years. This is of little consequence to those able spellers who have good visual recall. But those who lack this natural ability need the security of good guide lines and strategies to help them to come to terms with the intricacies of our spelling structure.

'Spelling Rules !' is designed to cover general spelling rules. Each rule is carefully explained in 'user friendly' terms, and the accompanying worksheets will give further help and practice. Many of the rules overlap, and therefore reinforce each other.

1

Section Two of the book deals mainly with common digraphs and letter patterns. Included in this section is a number of mnemonics and memory joggers which provide additional help.

If a pupil can master basic spelling rules, then a firm foundation for writing will be laid, and he or she will be adequately prepared to tackle the more complicated rules as they appear at a later stage.

'Spelling Rules!' is targeted at pupils at the Key Stage Two level ie. seven to eleven year olds, but many older pupils may well benefit from its teaching.

HOW TO USE THIS BOOK

The English language is a complex structure. Over the centuries it has absorbed into its system many words and letter combinations from other countries. It is difficult to imagine that any regular spelling rules could ever be applied to our written language.

However, in spite of this assumption, it has been found that about seventy five per cent of the words in our language do in fact follow spelling rules.

'Spelling Rules !' is intended to show how a number of simple basic rules can be applied to a large proportion of the words we use. Of course there are exceptions. No rule is infallible. But students will find a great number of spelling problems will be solved by following the straightforward rules as they are presented. The book does not cover common high usage words which have irregular letter combinations. Many of these are dealt with in the Golden Key Spelling by Singing series (see description at the end of this book)

Some people can tell at a glance whether or not a word is spelt correctly. These lucky people may never need to learn a spelling rule. Others are not so fortunate. The best way for these people to conquer spelling problems is by learning to follow a structured programme which includes simple strategies and rules. In this way, they will grow in confidence and improvement in writing skills can be assured.

The worksheets in the book are intended to be used after careful teaching of each rule. They are of value as a check to ensure that each rule has been fully understood. Extension rules and teacher's notes are printed in smaller print at the foot of some spelling rule pages. It is left to the discretion of the teacher to decide if and when it would be appropriate to introduce these points to their pupils.

It is not essential to follow the rules and exercises, in the same order in which they appear in the book. However it is advisable to ensure that ALL users fully understand the section on Vowels and Syllables before moving on.

DO NOT ATTEMPT TO MASTER MORE THAN ONE RULE AT A TIME. IT MAY BE NECESSARY TO PRACTISE ONE RULE MANY TIMES. OTHERS WILL BE LEARNED QUICKLY AND EASILY.

It is important that those using the book should have a thorough knowledge of letter sounds, blends and digraphs. Part Two of the book is set aside to give a little extra practice and reinforcement to the learning of some of these letter patterns.

'Spelling Rules !' is aimed mainly at those at the Key Stage Two level. However, other students may well find the contents useful too.

Terms Used In this Book

LETTER BLENDS
Two or more consonants making one sound eg. **b r, s p r**

LETTER PATTERNS
A group of vowels and consonants making one sound eg. **i g h t, o u g h**

DIGRAPHS
Two vowels making one sound eg. **a i, o a**

KEY WORDS
High usage or basic words, many of which have unusual spellings eg. **would, people**

MNEMONICS
Memory aids.

VOWEL SYMBOLS
For short vowels ă eg. **măt**

For long vowels ā eg. **māte**

PART ONE

SPELLING RULES

CONTENTS

PART ONE - SPELLING RULES

RULES 1 - 3 7
Alphabet, Vowels, Syllables
RULES 4 - 5 15
Word roots, Doubling
RULES 6 - 10 21
Magic e, Suffixing
RULES 11 - 15 33
ck or ke, c,k, lk/nk/sk, ic
RULES 16 - 18 45
Short vowel endings
RULES 19 - 21 53
Words ending in le
RULES 22 - 23 61
ly, all/full/till
RULES 24 - 25 67
Shun, shal, shus
RULES 26 - 28 73
Final y
RULES 29 - 32 81
Soft g
RULE 33 91
'w' rules
RULES 34 - 35 95
Plurals

SPELLING RULES 1 - 3

ALPHABET

VOWELS

SYLLABLES

Rule 1 . . . . The alphabet

Rule 2 . . . . Long and short vowels

Rule 3 . . . . Syllables

RULE 1

THE ALPHABET

There are twenty six letters in the alphabet.

Upper case letters
A B C D E F G H I J K L M N O P Q R S T U V W X Y Z

Lower case letter
a b c d e f g h i j k l m n o p q r s t u v w x y z

It is important to learn the correct sequence of these letters. This is very useful when using such things as a dictionary, telephone directory, catalogue or filing system.

Five of the letters are called **vowels - a e i o u** . The remaining twenty one letters are called **consonants.** The letter **y** is used as a consonant at the beginning of words such as **y**ester-day, **y**oung etc. But letter **y** can also be used at the end of a word in place of a vowel. It replaces letter **e** in words like ver**y**, happ**y** etc, and it replaces letter **i** in words like tr**y** and cr**y**.

The vowels are the most important letters of all, as at least one of them (or letter **y**) appear in every single syllable of every word which we write.

You should remember that in general, words in the English language do not end with the letters.

i , j , v or q

ALPHABET

How many letters are there in the alphabet ?...............

Write the letters of the alphabet in the correct order using capital (upper case) letters.

....

Write the letters of the alphabet using lower case letters.

....

Which letter comes in the middle of the alphabet ?...........

Which letter comes before J ?...............................

Which letter comes after S ?................................

Put these groups of letters in alphabetical order.

S L Q M D R...

B X E N Y A...

K O U F H C...

Which are the vowels ?....................................

Write two words where letter Y is used as a consonant at the beginning of a word.

....

RULE 2

LONG AND SHORT VOWELS

As so many spelling rules are based on a knowledge of long and short vowels, it is important to be able to distinguish between the two sounds made by each vowel. We mark the short vowels like this ˘ .

These are **ă ĕ ĭ ŏ ŭ** as heard in this sentence.

Săm mĕt Tĭm ŏn Sŭnday.

The long vowels are marked like this ¯ . We hear the long vowel sounds **ā ē ī ō ū** in this sentence.

Plāy mē nīne ōld tūnes.

Practise listening to, and identifying the long or short vowel sounds in these words

tăp	**tāpe**
pĭn	**pīne**
nŏt	**nōte**
cŭb	**cūbe**

LONG AND SHORT VOWELS

Read the sentences carefully, and mark all short vowel **sounds** with this mark ˘ eg că̆t.

1. Sam and Ben have been to the match.
2. Kim hid in the hut with the cat.
3. Did Tom have his bat with him?
4. Mum went to the shop to get six buns.
5. Will you chop the wood for me?

Now read these sentences, and mark all the long vowel **sounds** like this ˉ eg cāme.

1. Jane came home on the tube.
2. Save me some of your cake.
3. I hope Clive likes his prize.
4. June and Kate will go home by tube.
5. Jake will play a tune on his flute.

Now mark all the long and short vowel **sounds** in these sentences. Remember, it is the **sounds** of the vowels which you are looking for. Do not mark silent vowels.

1. John has lost his black blazer.
2. Can you find five red cubes?
3. I had to run to catch the nine o'clock bus.
4. It is late and so I am going to bed.
5. He had chips and chops on his plate.

Mark all the long and short vowel **sounds** in these words.

dog hat make stable clock globe same take jug sit like pin cube hop hope ride stop run

RULE 3

SYLLABLES

A **syllable** is a beat of a word. Words can be of one or more **syllables**. Listen for the beats in these words. Tap out the number of beats you can hear.

cat.................................one syllable

be-gan.........................two syllables

car-a-van.....................three syllables

op-tim-ist-ic.................four syllables

Every syllable must contain one vowel or vowel digraph (two vowels together making one sound like **ai** **oa** etc)

Breaking a long word into syllables helps to make the spelling easier. You can tackle one small part at a time. Check to see that you have a vowel (or digraph) in each syllable.

SYLLABLES

1. Divide these words into syllables. Underline all the vowels.

banana.....................ba-na-na   fantastic.................................

splendid...........................   Atlantic..................................

sandal..............................   distracted...............................

2. Join the syllable - one from each column - to make real words.
Write out the words you have made.

pad   ted   ....

con   bit   ....

mel   sect   ....

rab   let   ....

tab   vict   ....

in   lock   ....

3. Put the syllables in the correct order to make real words

phant-e-el.........................ad-ture-ven.......................

ter-af-noon.......................bat-ac-ra ....

sen-ted-pre..........................

13

RULES 4 - 5

WORD ROOTS

DOUBLING

Rule 4..........................Word roots

Rule 5..........................Doubling

RULE 4

WORD ROOTS

The ROOT of a word is the part which gives the meaning. Word endings (suffixes) or word beginnings (prefixes) may be added to word ROOTS.

Look at the word dis**appear**ance. You will see the root of the word is **appear**. The prefix **dis** and the suffix **ance** have been added.

Look at the ROOTS of these words.

en**light**en

un**guard**ed

mis**manage**ment

dis**trust**

WORD ROOTS

Underline the Word Roots in these words. Then write out each whole word, leaving a space between the prefixes, the ROOTS and the suffixes.

besiege.............................be-siege

friendly............................

fashionable.........................

assistance..........................

unfriendly..........................

misunderstanding....................

disappearance.......................

remarkable..........................

unharmed............................

development.........................

hopeless............................

RULE 5
DOUBLING

A **suffix** is the word given to a 'word ending' which is added to an existing word. There are lots of **suffixes**. Amongst the most commonly used are - **ing, ed, er, est, en, ance, ence, y, ment, less,** and **le**.

In order to keep a vowel **short** when adding a suffix, there must always be **two consonants** between the short vowel and the suffix. If the root word ends in a single consonant, this must always be **doubled** before adding the suffix.

> rŭn + ing.............................rŭ**nn**ing

> hŏp + ing............................hŏ**pp**ing

If there are already TWO CONSONANTS between the short vowel and the suffix, then doubling is not necessary.

> jŭmp + ed..............................jŭ**mp**ed

> stănd + ing............................stă**nd**ing

To help you to remember this rule, sing this rhyme to the tune of `One man went to mow'

> Short vowels have TWO letters
> Before you add an ending.
> Always remember this rule,
> Before you add an ending.

TEACHER'S NOTE
Remember the following consonants can never be doubled - **w, v,**

18

DOUBLING

Remember to double the consonant in short vowel words before you add an ending.

Add the root word and the suffix together and write out the whole word. Do not forget to double the consonant, if necessary.

bump + ed.....................stop + ed......................

help + er.....................big + est......................

want + ed.....................flat + en......................

sun + y.....................jump + er......................

rest + ing.....................swim + er......................

cut + ing.....................spin + ing......................

Complete the following sentences. Remember to double the consonant, if necessary.

1.   The horse jump + ed.....................over the gate.

2.   I was run + ing.....................to catch the bus.

3.   At the end of the show, everyone clap + ed.....................

4.   This swim + er.....................is the win + er.....................

5.   The tree was bend + ing.....................over in the gale.

6.   The people stamp + ed.....................their feet to keep warm

7.   The little dog wag + ed his tail.....................in excitement.

8.   The children were spend + ing.....................their pocket money

Add a double consonant to complete the following words

bu.......le   po.......y   ra.......le

su.......en   flo.......y   bu.......er

gi.......le   ha.......en   we.......ing

wo.......le   mu.......le   ha.......y

pu.......ing   je.....y   pu.......le

RULES 6 - 10

MAGIC e

SUFFIXING

Rule 6.............. Magic **e**

Rule 7.............. **ie, oe, ue**

Rule 8............. Adding '**ing**' to magic **e**

Rule 9............. Dropping **e** before suffixes beginning with a vowel

Rule 10........... Keeping **e** before suffixes beginning with a consonant.

RULE 6

MAGIC e

Magic **e** comes at the end of words, IT IS ALWAYS SILENT. Magic **e** shoots magic sparks over one letter and changes short vowels into long vowels.

tăp changes to **tāpe**

nŏt changes to **nōte**

fĭn changes to **fīne**

MAGIC e

Write out the following words, then add a magic **e** to each word you have written. Mark all the long and short vowels like this

tăp   tāpe

can..............   win..................

hop..............   cap..................

fin..............   mat.................

pin..............   cut..................

kit..............   not..................

Circle the word which fits each sentence.

These apples are not (rip ripe).
The children went on a seaside (tripe trip).
We will go for a picnic if it is (fine fine).
We decided to go by (tub tube) to London.
Jane left a (not note) for her mother.
She had to (mop mope) up the spilt milk.
Tom went out to fly his (kite kit).
The kittens were very (cute cut)
I (hop hope) to see you soon.
A dreadful (din dine) was coming from the classroom

Put a magic **e** word into each sentence.

Kim was l............ for school.
The dog jumped over the g.............
Hang the washing on the l...............
Rounders can be a very exciting g...............
The snowman had a p............ in his mouth.

23

RULE 7

MORE ABOUT MAGIC e

In some words, Magic **e** stands directly next to the vowel. Here are some sentences to help you to remember these important words.

ie

Do not l**ie**. Your t**ie** is in the p**ie**.

oe

Poor old J**oe** hurt his t**oe** on the h**oe**.

ue

Don't contin**ue** to arg**ue**. It is tr**ue** that S**ue** ate the bl**ue** gl**ue** on T**ue**sday.
To the resc**ue** at the barbec**ue** with tiss**ue**.
The letter is d**ue** on T**ue**sday

Teacher's Notes
Making sketches to illustrate these sentences will help to reinforce **ie** **oe** and **ue**.

MORE ABOUT MAGIC **e**

ie, oe, ue,

Add **ie,oe** or **ue** to the following letters to make them into words.

barbec............   tr..............

p.................   l..............

resc...............   tiss..........

t.................   arg............

contin...........   bl..............

S.................   gl..............

d................   T.......sday

Use the above words to answer these questions

Not false.........................   Worn round the neck...................

A sticky substance..................   Something to eat........................

A girl`s name......................   The name of a day.....................

To carry on.........................   To quarrel................................

Part of the foot....................   Owing.....................................

An outdoor meal....................   A colour...................................

To save someone..................   To tell an untruth....................

25

RULE 8

ADDING ing TO WORDS ENDING IN e

Here is a rhyme to help you to remember this rule.

Words that end with the letter **e**
Drop the **e** before **i-n-g**

take...............taking

move..............moving

ADDING ing TO WORDS ENDING IN e

Change these words into **ing** words. **Do not forget to drop the e first**

drive......driving   hope...................

make...................   bake...................

smile...................   have...................

dance.................   taste...................

shake.................   joke...................

Now make the words in brackets into **ing** words

1. I enjoy singing and (dance).......................

2. I was (hope)...................... you would come.

3. Emma is (take)....................her friend with her.

4. John will be (take)............... his (drive)................test.

5. Everyone helped with the (bake).........................

6. James is (choose)..................... new boots.

7. The tramp was (smoke).....................a clay pipe.

8. Sarah was coughing and (sneeze).....................

9. Will you be (come)..................... to see me ?

10. The meal was set in the (dine)................... room.

27

RULE 9

DROPPING e BEFORE SUFFIXES BEGINNING WITH A VOWEL

This is an easy rule. Do you remember the rhyme ?

> Words that end with the letter **e**
> Drop the **e** before **i-n-g** (See Rule 8)

In fact, letter **e** is nearly always dropped before those suffixes which start with a vowel. - **ing, ance, able**, etc.

    move + able....................movable

    persevere + ance..............perseverance

IMPORTANT EXCEPTION TO THIS RULE (see also section on Soft **c** and Soft **g**)

Words which end with **ce** or **ge** keep the **e** before 'able' in order to keep the **c** and **g** soft.

    manage + able...................manag**e**able
    notice + able.....................notic**e**able

28

DROPPING **e** BEFORE SUFFIXES
BEGINNING WITH A VOWEL

Add the suffixes to the words below. Don't forget to drop the **e** where necessary. Watch out for words ending in **ce** or **ge** before **able.**

move + ing...................... bite + ing...........................

notice + able.................. save + ed............................

tire + ed...................... trace + able.......................

amuse + ing.................. change + able....................

safe + est.................. hope + ing.......................

service + able.................. wise + est...........................

close + est.................... ripe + en...........................

use + ing...................... use + able..........................

love + able..................... manage + able...................

strive + ing.................... desire + able.......................

RULE 10

KEEPING e BEFORE SUFFIXES STARTING WITH A CONSONANT

Here are some suffixes (word endings) which start with a consonant.

less, ly, ness, ment, ful, teen

If the root word ends in an **e**, the **e** remains before a suffix which starts with a consonant.

hope...............hope**less**

hope...............hope**ful**

life...............life**less**

nine...............nine**teen**

safe...............safe**ly**

amaze.............amaze**ment**

Teacher's Notes

Just a reminder. Look again at Rule 10. Remember to drop the **e** if the suffix begins with a vowel.

30

KEEPING e BEFORE SUFFIXES STARTING WITH A CONSONANT

Add the suffix to these word roots, and write out the word you have made. Remember the rule for suffixes that start with a consonant.

nine + ty..................   strange + ly..............

smoke + less...............   waste + ful...............

love + ly..................   manage + ment.............

Now for a mixture. Remember when to drop the '**e**', and when to keep the '**e**'

amuse + ing........................... amuse + ment.............................

live + ly................................ live + ing.....................................

hope + ed.............................. hope + ful...................................

move + ing........................... move + ment.............................

peace + ful........................... nice + ly.....................................

sense + less........................... sense + ible.................................

use + ing.............................. use + ful.....................................

lone + ly..........................

RULES 11 - 15

ck or ke,c,k,ic

Rule 11.......... **ck** or **ke**

Rule 12.......... **lk, nk, sk,** at the end of a word

Rule 13.......... Final **k** after digraphs

Rule 14.......... **k** or **c** at the beginning of a word

Rule 15.......... **ic** at the end of a word

33

RULE 11

ck and ke

ck is used only when it immediately follows a SHORT vowel. ie in words which have an **ăck, ĕck, ĭck, ŏck,** or **ŭck** sound

blăck, nĕck, stĭck, rŏck, lŭck

Suffixes (word endings) may be added to words containing these sounds like this

blă**ck**er, stĭ**ck**er, rŏ**ck**et, bŭ**ck**et

NEVER USE **ck** AFTER A LONG VOWEL. After long vowels, use **ke**.

Watch how the spelling changes, as the vowel sound changes.

bă**ck**	changes to	bā**ke**
lĭ**ck**	changes to	lī**ke**
dŭ**ck**	changes to	dū**ke**

ck and ke

Put a **ck** word into each of these sentences

1. Please remember to ....the door.
2. I had a ....when I saw how late it was.
3. John had to walk with a ....after the accident.
4. When no one answered the front door, the visitor went round to the ....
5. The children went to feed the ....in the park.

Put a **ke** word into each of these sentences

1. Please ....your things with you when you leave.
2. Some children do not ....green vegetables.
3. Everyone laughed at the comedien's ....
4. The ....and duchess lived in a splendid castle.
5. Ben went for a long ride on his b.................

Circle the correct **ck** or **ke** words in these sentences.

1. She went into the garden to (pike pick) flowers.
2. Emma had a quick (snack snake) for lunch.
3. There was a huge (bloke block) of wood by the door.
4. For goodness (sack sake) do not tell anyone.
5. The kitten began to (like lick) the dish.
6. A long (snack snake) wriggled through the grass.
7. Mary took her books (bake back) to the library.
8. The man hammered a long (stake stack) in the ground.
9. A huge (pike pick) was swimming in the river.
10. The tramp lived in an old (shake shack).

Add **ck** or **ke** to these letters. Look out for the long or short vowel marks.

br ĭ..... b ī...... l ā....... bl ă...... d ū......
b ā...... sh ā......

35

RULE 12

lk, nk, sk ENDINGS

These endings, like **ck** come immediately after SHORT VOWELS.

Please note, **THE LETTER C IS NEVER INCLUDED IN THESE LETTER BLENDS**

l k	**n k**	**s k**
mĭ**lk**	sĭ**nk**	dĕ**sk**
sĭ**lk**	bŭ**nk**	rĭ**sk**
sŭ**lk**	drĭ**nk**	brĭ**sk**

lk, nk, sk

Add **lk** to the following letters.

mi........   si.......   su.........   bu.......   hu........

Make up sentences for three of these words

1 ....
2 ....
3 ....

Add **nk** to these letters

dri......   tru.......   bli.....   sa......   shri......
wi........   ba........   si......   dru.....   thi.......
tha......   spa.......   ta......   bu......   dra.......

Add **sk** to these letters

de......   fri......y   du.......   ru.......   tu.......   ri......

Add an **lk**, **nk**, or **sk** word to these sentences
1. Elephants have ivory tu........s.
2. Growing children should dri..... mi...... every day.
3. The spider weaves a si.....en thread to make its web.
4. It is polite to say tha...... you.
5. The professor was seated at his de......
6. She worked hard from dawn till du.......
7. Anne decided to open a ba....... account.
8. Her jumper had shru... in the washing machine.
9. This answer is wrong. You must thi...... again.
10. The sudden bright light made her bli.......

RULE 13

MORE ABOUT FINAL k

Letter **k** stands alone at the end of words if it follows 'vowel pairs' (**ee, oo, ea** etc) or 'r' pairs (**ar, er, ir, or, ur**)

ee.......s**ee**k   oo............l**oo**k

oa......s**oa**k   ea............sp**ea**k

or......c**or**k   ar............p**ar**k

NEVER USE ck AFTER THESE LETTER PAIRS

MORE ABOUT FINAL k

Can you find these words in the Wordsearch puzzle ?

park   dark   spark   pork   fork   speak   leak   squeak
cloak   soak   croak   seek   week   look   book

The words may be found across or down

A	D	A	R	K	P	D	E	C
S	E	E	K	L	O	O	K	L
B	C	S	P	A	R	K	X	O
H	G	S	A	F	K	C	L	A
J	F	O	R	K	M	R	E	K
W	L	A	K	I	S	O	A	K
E	M	K	S	P	E	A	K	N
E	S	Q	U	E	A	K	P	Q
K	R	V	B	O	O	K	S	T

RULE 14

k or C AT THE BEGINNING OF A WORD

Only start a word with **k** if the next letter is **e** or **i**. Think of **Ke**vin's **ki**tten.

ke	ki
kettle	kitten
kedgeree	kill
kestrel	kick
key	king
keep	kind

At all other times, use **c**. If the next letter is **a**, **o**, or **u**, then use **c**

cat	cot	cut
cap	cow	cup

If the next letter is **l** or **r,** then use **c**.

clap	crash
clog	cream
clean	croak

40

k OR c AT THE BEGINNING OF A WORD

Put **k** or **c** at the beginning of these words

_ ing	_ ettle	_ lean
_ ow	_ rab	_ eep
_ ut	_ ill	_ ept
_ andle	_ ind	_ astle

Complete these sentences by adding **k** or **C** to the unfinished words.

1. The _ ing was _ rowned at the _ astle.

2. _ evin _ icked the ball into the _ rowd.

3. _ an you _ ome with _ im and me to feed the _ ows ?

4. My _ at _ eeps her _ ittens in the _ itchen.

5. Try and - eep your _ lothes _ lean.

6. The _ ind _ aretaker lit the _ andle so that we _ ould find our way to the _ loakroom.

7. _ arol _ ept some _ ream _ ake in the _ upboard.

RULE 15

ic AT THE END OF A WORD

If the sound **ick** is heard at the end of a word containing two or more syllables, then the final **k** is dropped.

THIS ONLY APPLIES TO **ick** WORDS

mag-ic   Atlant-ic   Domin-ic

trag-ic   Pacif-ic   top-ic

NOUNS (naming words) which end in **ic** can be made into **adjectives** (describing words) simply by adding **al**.

music-al ....   musical

mechanic-al ......   mechanical

politic-al ....   political

comic-al ....   comical

42

ic AT THE END OF A WORD

1. Add **ic** to these letters, and write out the word you have made.

    gigant__   ....

    histor__   ....

    mag__   ....

    idiot__   ....

    patriot__   ....

    enthusiast__   ....

2. Now use one of the above words to fit each of these descriptions.

    Loving one's country ....

    Enormous   ....

    Very keen   ....

    Stupid   ....

    Secret powers   ....

    Ancient   ....

43

RULES 16 - 18

SHORT VOWEL ENDINGS

Rule 16...........Flossy words (ff, ll, ss)

Rule 17...........tch

Rule 18...........dge

RULE 16
FLOSSY WORDS

Short words containing a short vowel and ending in **f, l,** or **s,** always double the last letter. We call these FLOSSY words.

ff cŭff, clĭff, ŏff, stĭff

ll hĭll, pĭll, stĭll, dŏll

ss tŏss, crŏss, drĕss, mĕss

IMPORTANT EXCEPTIONS

yes, bus, if, until

Teacher's Notes,

It is rare to find other double consonants at the end of short words. A few notable exceptions are -

egg ebb add buzz fizz

FLOSSY WORDS

Remember to put **ff**, **ll**, or **ss** after short vowels.

1. Add **l** or **ll** to these letters. Write out the words you have made.

    foo __ ....   sti__ ....   hee__ ....

    i__ ....   too__ ....   snai__ ....

    do__ ....   be__ ....   tai__ ....

2. Add **f** or **ff** to these letters and write out the word you have made.

    sti__ ....   lea__ ....   scar__ ....

    hoo__ ....   stu__ ....   bee__ ....

    pu__ ....   loa__ ....   cli__ ....

3. Add **s** or **ss** to these letters, and write out the words you have made.

    cat__ ....   pet__ ....   to__ ....

    fork__ ....   mo__ ....   hi__ ....

    le__ ....   card__ ....   lamp__ ....

47

RULE 17

tch

Add **t** to **ch** immediately after a SHORT VOWEL. When you hear the sound of a**tch**, e**tch**, i**tch**, o**tch** or u**tch**, then use **tch**

ă**tch**	mă**tch**, hă**tch**, că**tch**
ĕ**tch**	fĕ**tch**
ĭ**tch**	hĭ**tch**, wĭ**tch**
ŏ**tch**	hŏp-scŏ**tch**
ŭ**tch**	hŭ**tch**, crŭ**tch**

At all other times, use **ch** - after all **double vowels**, **vowel digraphs**, **r** pairs (**ar, er, ir, or, ur**) and after **n**.

b**ee**ch p**ea**ch, c**oa**ch c**ou**ch m**ar**ch p**or**ch
ch**ur**ch cru**n**ch

IMPORTANT EXCEPTIONS

much such rich which

48

tch

Underline all the **tch** words in this poem.

> A witch in the kitchen
> Doing a bit of stitching.
> There's a scratch
> As she lights a match,
> Sews on a patch.
> Climbs through the hatch,
> Snatches a batch of watches,
> Can you catch her ?
>
> Now here's a hitch,
> Where is that witch ?
>
> In the ditch ?
>
> No by the hutch
> Waving a crutch.
> Fetch her. Fetch her. Fetch her.

Add **tch** or **ch** to these letters to make real words. Remember, only use **tch** after SHORT VOWELS. Watch out for the exceptions.

pin__	tor__	la___
mar__	ca___	lun__
chur__	ri__	ben__
mu__	pea__	wi___
sti___	cou__	pa___

49

RULE 18

dge

If a word ends with a **j** sound, always use **ge**. No word in the English language ends with the letter **J**. (see Rule 1)

The **dge** rule is exactly the same as that used for **tch** (rule 17) Add **d** to **ge** immediately after a SHORT VOWEL. If you hear the sound of a**dge**, e**dge**, i**dge**, o**dge**, or u**dge**, then always use **dge.**

ă**dge**	bă**dge**
ĕ**dge**	hĕ**dge**
ĭ**dge**	brĭ**dge**
ŏ**dge**	lŏ**dge**
ŭ**dge**	bŭ**dge**

At all other times, use **ge** - after long vowels, after the **r** pairs (**ar, er, ir, or, ur**) and after **n**

c**a**ge h**u**ge l**ar**ge m**er**ge b**ir**ch g**or**ge s**ur**ge
hi**n**ge

dge

Answer all these clues with a **dge** word

1. Something to ride on in the snow ....

1. An animal with a black and white striped head
   ....

3. A sort of shelf l...........................

4. To move about quickly d......................

5. To move out of the way b......................

6. A place to keep food cool ....

7. A small emblem worn on a coat or jacket............

8. A row of small trees or shrubs.......................

Add **ge** or **dge** to these letters to make real words.

smu___   hu__   plun__

sta__   pa__   le___

ra__   stran__   lar__

he___   bri___   fri___

RULES 19 - 21

WORDS ENDING IN le

Rule 19.............Words ending in **le**

Rule 20.............Words ending in **stle**

Rule 21...........Words ending in **able**
or **ible**

RULE 19

WORDS ENDING IN le

When the sound **ul** or **el** is heard at the end of a word, it is NEARLY ALWAYS spelt **le**. So remember

IF IN DOUBT, USE le.

le is used like other suffixes, and therefore the doubling rule must always be applied after SHORT VOWELS (see Rule 5)
If there are already two consonants between the short vowel and **le**, then there is no need for doubling.

bŭbb-**le**	crŭmb-**le**
mĕdd-**le**	hănd-**le**

After long vowels

crād-**le**

stāb-**le**

tāb-**le**

WORDS ENDING IN le

Answer all these clues with an **le** word. Remember, SHORT VOWELS need TWO consonants before the **le** ending - you may need to double the consonant. Long vowel words have only ONE consonant before the **le** ending.

1.   A baby sleeps in this ....

2.   You can blow this using soap and water ....

2.   Made of wax. Gives us light ....

4.   Where meals are laid ....

5.   To complain gr...

7.   Used when sewing ....

8.   A fruit a...

9.   Very easy s...

10. Used to open a door ....

11. A horse lives in one ....

12. A mouse might do this to cheese n....................................

13. A weed which stings ....

14. A fight between armies b...

15. A leather seat used by a horse rider ....

RULE 10

stle ENDINGS

A few important **le** words contain a silent **t**. Don't worry. There aren't many of these. Here are the ones you are most likely to meet.

wrestle whistle thistle trestle castle bristle hustle bustle jostle

Here is a rhyme which may help you to remember some of these words

Look out for the silent T

In castle, wrestle, whistle

Watch out, here it comes again

In hustle, bustle, thistle

stle ENDINGS

Look for the following words in this Wordsearch puzzle.

wrestle, hustle, whistle, thistle, jostle, castle, trestle and **bristle**

The words may be found across, down or diagonally

B	H	S	J	W	S	T	R	S
R	U	T	R	O	I	E	H	T
I	S	W	H	I	S	T	L	E
S	T	J	I	I	T	T	E	S
T	L	S	W	L	S	L	L	R
L	E	T	R	E	S	T	L	E
E	J	H	C	A	S	T	L	E
B	W	R	E	S	T	L	E	E

RULE 21
able and ible

able is a very useful suffix. (see Rule 9). It means

'**fit for**'.**able** is always added to a complete word.

      accept + able ....   accept**able**
      understand + able ...   understand**able**
      profit + able ....   profit**able**

Drop FINAL **e** before **able** (see Rule 9)
      love + able ....   lov**able**
      value + able ....   valu**able**

Change **y** to **i** before **able** (see Rule 27)
      rely + able ....   reli**able**
      justify + able ....   justifi**able**

Adding **able** to words ending in **ce** or **ge** (see Rules 31 and 32). These words keep Final **e** before adding **able**
      manage + able .... manage**able**
      notice + able........... notice**able**

ible

ible is a suffix which is added only to a non word, **ible** always follows a consonant.

      poss + ible ....   poss**ible**
      vis + ible ....   vis**ible**
      terr + ible ....   terr**ible**

able and ible

Make the following, into **able** words. Do not forget to drop the **e** if necessary. Do not forget to change **y** to **i**.

accept + able ....

rely + able ....

love + able ....

understand + able ....

manage + able ....

justify + able ....

notice + able ....

change + able ....

believe + able..................................

Choose an **ible** word from the list below, to fit into these sentences.

The house was just .... through the fog.

Is it ....to bring dogs into this hotel ?

It was .... to lift the heavy box.

That was a very .... suggestion.

This food is not ....

impossible edible visible sensible permissible

59

RULES 22 - 23

ly, all, full, till

Rule 22 .... ly endings

Rule 23.................... all/al
full/ful
till/til

RULE 22

WORDS ENDING IN ly

ly is an important suffix (word ending) which is always added to a whole word. PLEASE NOTE THERE IS NO **e** IN THIS SUFFIX.

sad + ly.......... sad**ly**

safe + ly......... safe**ly**

sure + ly......... sure**ly**

Change **y** to **i** before **ly** (see Rule 27)

ready + ly........ readi**ly**

happy + ly........ happi**ly**

If the existing word ends in **l**, the **l** is retained when **ly** is added, thus making **lly**

beautiful + ly.... beautiful**ly**

gradual + ly....... gradual**ly**

careful + ly........ careful**ly**

62

WORDS ENDING IN **ly**

Add **ly** to these words. Remember the **y** to **i** rule.

sad + ly ....beautiful + ly..........................

steady + ly....................hopeful + ly..........................

happy + ly....................safe + ly..............................

Put one of the above words into each of the sentences below.

They all lived ....ever after.

She reached the other side of the river ....

The dancer performed ....

They held the rope ....

.... she will visit us next week if she is well enough.

The child looked ....at the broken doll.

RULE 23

all and full

all and **full** are words which can stand alone. However, if either of these is added to another word or syllable, then one **l** is dropped

al-ways	dread-**ful**
al-so	hope-**ful**
al-together	aw-**ful**
al-ready	use-**ful**
al-most	beauti-**ful**

till

The word **till** drops an **l** in the word **until**.

all full till

Put in the correct **al** words from the list below.

All powerful ....

It was very cold .... the sun was shining.

Forever ....

Nearly ....

When the alarm was raised, the building was
.... blazing.

already   almost   almighty   although   always

Put in the correct **ful** word from the list below.

She was .... to have her umbrella with her.

The celebration was a .... occasion.

After the accident, she had a ....bruise.

These tools have proved to be very ....

As it was such a .... morning, they went
down to the   beach

painful   beautiful   joyful   thankful   useful

Put the word **until** into these sentences.

We will have to wait .... it stops raining.

Stand over there .... the bus comes.

He shouted .... he was hoarse.

65

RULES 24 - 25

WORDS ENDING IN A 'shun' 'shal' or 'shus' SOUND

Rule 24 ....**tion/sion**

Rule 25.................**cian/cial/cious**

RULE 24

tion and sion

The **shun** sound at the end of a word is nearly always spelt **tion**. When you hear this sound at the end of a word, never be tempted to use **sh**. There are only two words which use **shion** as a word ending. These two words are fa**shion** and cu**shion**. **tion** comes after the long vowels **ā, ē, ō,** and **ū**. It also comes after the short vowel **ĭ**, and after letter **c**.

ā... na**tion**	ē... comple**tion**
ō... po**tion**	ū... solu**tion**
ĭ... addi**tion**	c... frac**tion**

sion

When you hear the sound **zyun** at the end of a word, it is usually spelt **sion**.

televi**sion**	confu**sion**
occa**sion**	revi**sion**

TEACHER'S NOTES

Although **tion** is the most common spelling for **shun**, it would be as well to note the following alternatives.

sion after **n** in words like man**sion**, pen**sion**, exten**sion**.

ssion after short vowels in words like expre**ssion**, confe**ssion**.

tion and sion

Listen for the **tion** (shun) sound or the **sion** (zyun) sound.
Put the correct endings to these words.

na_____   solu____

televi____   pollu____

deci____   explo____

commo____   ac____

revi____   revolu____

tradi____   confu____

Put a **tion** or **sion** ending to the words in these sentences.

There was confu____ everywhere after the explo____

I watched Televi____ instead of doing some revi____ for
the examina____

There was a commo____ at the sta____ and I missed my
connec____

I had to make a deci____ about whether I would join the
expedi____

69

RULE 25

cian (shan)

cian is pronounced **shan**. It is the word ending which tells you that someone is an expert. You will notice that all the root words end with **ic**.

An expert in mus**ic** is a musi**cian**

An expert in mag**ic** is a magi**cian**

Also - opti**cian** physi**cian** politi**cian** techni**cian**

cial (shal)

This word ending is pronounced **shal**. NEVER spell this word ending with **sh** unless you are writing the word mar**shal**. This is the only word using this letter pattern.

finan**cial** spe**cial** artifi**cial** offi**cial**

cious (shus)

Again, as above, this **ci** word ending has a **sh** sound - **shus** . But it is NEVER spelt with **sh**

pre**cious** vi**cious** deli**cious** spa**cious**

TEACHER'S NOTES
Watch out for these; **tial** (shal) - par**tial**, ini**tial**, essen**tial**, poten**tial tious** (shus) - ambi**tious**, infec**tious**, supersti**tious**, **tient** (shunt) - pa**tient**.

70

cian cial cious

Unscramble these **cian** words. Remember **cian** is the 'expert' ending.

leercticina................... oaptilicin.....................

ntcioiap .... ngcamaii ....

icumsian .... acncithein...................

Fill in the missing letters in these **cial** words

soc___   finan__al

offi____   artifi___l

spe_i__   espe___lly

Put two of these words into sentences of your own.

....

....

Find the correct **cious** words to answer these clues.

valuable.................. spiteful.....................

awful.................... distrustful..................

lots of room............. pleasant to eat...............

spacious atrocious precious suspicious vicious delicious

71

RULES 26 - 28

FINAL y

Rule 26 .... Final **y** sounds

Rule 27............ Changing **y** to **i**

Rule 28............ **ay, ey, oy, uy**

RULE 26

FINAL y

Remember that no word in the English language, apart from some people's names, ends with the letter **i**. (see Rule 1) At the end of a word, the sound of **i** is nearly always spelt with letter **y**.

m**y** b**y** repl**y** tr**y** cr**y** wh**y**

At the end of a word with two or more syllables, the sound of **e** is spelt with letter **y**.

ver**y** happ**y** greed**y** grump**y**

Use this rhyme as a reminder

> If you can hear
> **e** or **i**
> At the end of a word,
> Then use letter **y**.

TEACHER'S NOTES
Letter **e** sounding its name, only comes at the end of these short words - he, me, we, she. Use **ee** in - see, tree, bee,
Watch out for the sound of **i** at the end of these words - pie, lie, tie, die (see Rule 7). The sound of **i** comes at the end of - high, sigh.

FINAL y

Remember at the end of a word, Final **y** can sound like **i**.
Make a sketch to remind you of this rule.

Oh m**y**, a fl**y** went b**y** in the sk**y**. I wonder wh**y**.

Remember at the end of words, Final **y** can sound like **e**.
Make a sketch to remind you of this rule.

A ver**y** happ**y** lad**y** with a greed**y** grump**y** bab**y**

RULE 27

CHANGE **y** TO **i**

Change **y** to **i** and add **es**
baby...........bab-ies

change **y** to **i** and add **ed**
marry..........marr-ied

change **y** to **i** and add **er**
carry..........carr-ier

change **y** to **i** and add **est**
happy..........happ-iest

change **y** to **i** and add **able**
rely............rel-iable

change **y** to **i** and add **ful**
mercy..........merc-iful

change **y** to **i** and add **ly**
ready..........read-ily

change **y** to **i** and add **less**
mercy..........merc-iless

change **y** to **i** and add **ess**
lazy...........laz-iness

change **y** to **i** and add **ment**
merry..........merr-iment

BUT - IF THE ENDING IS **ing**. THEN THE **y** MUST REMAIN

cry..........   cry-ing
try..........   try-ing
marry........   marry-ing
apply........   apply-ing

76

CHANGE y TO i

Change the words in brackets so that they have an **es**, **ed**, **er**, or an **est** ending

Yesterday, they were (marry)..................

The (lorry)............ drove too fast through the village.

They put the shopping in a (carry)...................bag.

It was the (happy).................day of her life.

Tom (cry).................when he fell over.

Change the words in brackets to words with **less**, **ly**, **ness**, or **ment** endings.

We wish you joy and (happy)....................................

He answered her (grumpy)....................................

In her anger she was quite (mercy)..............................

The atmosphere was one of (merry)............................

Add an **ing** ending to the words in these sentences.
Do not forget the rule for adding **ing** to words ending in **y**.

The birds were (fly).................... South.

I am (reply).............. to her letter today.

The washing was (dry)................ on the line.

She found the girl (spy)..............through the keyhole.

RULE 28

WORDS ENDING IN
ay, ey, oy, uy

This is a very easy rule. Words ending in **ay**, **ey**, **oy**, or **uy**, do not change when adding an ending.

p**ay**-ing   k**ey**-s   j**oy**-less   g**uy**-s

p**ay**-ment   ob**ey**-ing   empl**oy**-ment   b**uy**-ing

st**ay**-ing

st**ay**-ed

IMPORTANT EXCEPTION

Look out for **pay-ing** - BUT ....**paid**

78

WORDS ENDING IN
ay, ey, oy, uy

Add the endings to these words.

guy+s........................employ+ment................

play+ful....................stay+ing.....................

joy+less....................coy+ly.........................

You will need to have learned Rule 27 before attempting this next section.

Put the endings onto the words. Be careful.

happy+ness................... happy+ly.....................

enjoy+ment................... stay+ed......................

cry+ed....................... employ+ing...................

copy+ed...................... try+ed.......................

rely+ed...................... rely+ance....................

duty+es...................... ready+ly.....................

copy+ing..................... baby+es......................

RULES 29 - 32

SOFT c AND SOFT g

Rule 29.................. Soft **c** , soft **g**

Rule 30.................. To start a word with
soft **g** or **j**

Rule 31.................. **able** after soft **c** or
soft **g**

Rule 32.................. **ance** and **ence**

RULE 29

SOFT C AND SOFT g

You can hear the hard sound of **c** in these words

cat   **c**ot   **c**up

and the hard sound of **g** in these words

gate   **g**oat   **g**ull

The letter **c** is softened to an **s** sound, and the letter **g** softened to a **j** sound, if the following letters are **i** **y** or **e**.

Remember this rhyme

i, **y**, and **e**
Soften **c** and **g**

circus   **cy**cle   **ce**ntre

giant   **gy**mnast   **ge**rm

SOFT C AND SOFT g

Fill in the missing **i**, **y** or **e** letters into these words. Check your answers from the words at the end of the exercise.

c _ rcle	conc _ ert	c _ gnet	rec - ent
c _ cle	canc _ l	c - ty	dec - de

city, circle, decide, cancel, cygnet, recent, cycle, concert

Now do the same for these Soft **g** words.

g _ mnast	G _ rmany	garag _	Eg _ pt
eng _ ne	g _ ntle	g _ ant	g _ ng _ r

gentle, giant, ginger, Germany, gymnast, Egypt, engine, garage

Choose words from the foot of the page, to fit into these sentences.

The .... sold clothes pegs.

It was very dark down in the ....

The bus station is in the .... of the town.

The wizard had a .... wand.

There was a wooden ....round the garden.

We went to see the school ....

It is .... to skate on thin ....

Be very ....with the kitten.

gentle, dangerous, concert, centre, gypsy, ice, dungeon, fence, magic.

RULE 30

TO START A WORD WITH **g** OR **j**

The Soft **g** rule still applies (see Rule 29). If the next letter is **i**, **y**, or **e**, then use **g**.

ginger   **gy**mnast   **ge**neral

At all other times, use **j** - ie when the next letter is **a**, **o**, or **u**.

A **ja**r of **ja**m

Jump for **jo**y

Just **jo**gging

IMPORTANT EXCEPTION - **jelly**

TO START A WORD WITH **g** OR **j**

Put a **g** or **j** at the beginning of these words. Watch out for the exceptions.

_ug	_erm
_em	_ar
_entle	_ump
_elly	_oin
_ack	_ymnast

Fill in the missing **g**'s or **j**'s in these sentences.

_ane and the other girls went to _ermany.

The _ymnast was called _ack.

Although he looked fierce, the _iant was really very_entle.

_eorge likes _elly and _am.

Please bring me a _ug of _inger ale.

The _ypsy discovered the _ems when she _umped from the caravan.

RULE 31

able AFTER SOFT c AND SOFT g

Another easy one. When **ce** or **ge** come at the end of a word, the **e** must remain, before adding **able**. This is in order to keep the **c** and **g** soft.

These are probably the only ones you will need to remember -

service-**able**..............service**able**

notice-**able**..............notice**able**

manage-**able**...........manage**able**

change-**able**............change**able**

able AFTER SOFT c AND SOFT g

Make these words into **able** words.

manage_____

service_____

notice_____

change_____

By adding the prefix **un** at the beginning of these words, you can change the meaning. Write out the four words again, adding the prefix **un** to each of them.

....

....

Now put an **able** or an **un/able** word into these sentences. Use the words from the above exercises.

The tall man was very .... in the crowd.

The machine was so old, it was ....

Because the weather is so .... it is difficult to make a decision about the match.

RULE 32

ance AND ence

As these Soft **c** suffixes are so common, I have included them in this section (see also Rule 9).

If you wish to add **ance** or **ence** to a word, the rule is easy. If a word ends in **ant**, then use the **ance** ending. If the word ends in **ent**, then use the **ence** ending.

import-**ant**.........import**ance**

differ-**ent**...........differ**ence**

ance AND ence

Change these words into **ance** or **ence** words.

important ....   patient ....

dependent ....   relevant ....

extravagant ....   different ....

absent   ....   abundant ....

tolerant   ....   assistant ....

distant ....

Now using the above words, make two lists - one for **ance** words, and one for **ence** words.

ance   **ence**

RULE 33

w RULES

W RULES

These can be tricky, so you will need lots of practice. The letters following letter **w** often change their sounds.

w changes the sound of short **ă** into short **ŏ**.

was   **wa**nt   **wa**tch   **wa**sh

w changes the sound of **or** into the sound of **er.**

world   **wor**k   **wor**se   **wor**th

w changes the sound of **ar** into the sound of **or.**

warm   **war**   **war**n   **war**ble

W RULES

Remember, ă sounds like ŏ after **w**. Fill in the missing letters with
an **a** or **o**.

We do n _ t w_ nt to camp near the p _ nd.

When I g - t home, I w _ tched T _ p of the
P _ ps.

Yesterday, I w _ s stung by a w _ sp.

J _ hn had a w _ sh in h _ t water.

or sounds like **er** after **w**. Put **or** or **er** into these
sentences.

My moth __'s ring is w __ th a lot of money.

The robin is w __ king hard looking for w __ ms.

It took much long __ than he thought to complete his
w __ ld trip.

ar sounds like **or** after **w**. Put **ar** or **or** into these
sentences.

The teacher told the children a st __ y about the
w __ .

After the st __ m it became very w __ m.

This rew __ d is f __ Jim.

There was a st __ m w __ning on Sp __ts Day.

RULES 34 - 35

PLURALS

Rule 34............ Common plural endings

Rule 35............ Unusual plural endings

RULE 34

PLURALS

PLURAL means more than one. **PLURALS** are made in one of the following ways.

1. By adding an **s**. This is the most common way.

    cat + s...........cats   dog + s...........dogs

2. By adding **es** when you can hear **es** as a separate syllable, usually after **ss**, **sh**, **ch**, or **x**.

    fox + es........... foxes   dish + es..........dishes
    coach + es.........coaches dress + es.........dresses

3. By changing **y** or **i** and adding **es** (see Rule 27).

    baby + es..........babies

4. By adding **s** to words ending in **ay**, **ey**, **oy**, or **uy** (see Rule 28).

    day + s...........days   key + s.............keys
    boy + s...........boys   guy + s............ guys

5. Most words ending in **f**, change **f** to **v** and then add **es.**

    leaf.............leaves   knife............knives
    wolf..............wolves

PLURALS

Make these words into plurals by adding **s**.

cat _   gate _   door _   dog _   rabbit _

Make these words into plurals by adding **es**.

witch __   wish __   dress __   latch __   fox __

Make these words into plurals by changing **y** to **i** and adding **es**

lorry __   berry __   poppy __   lady __   duty _

Make these words into plurals by adding **s**.

boy _   day _   donkey _   guy _   way _

Make these words into plurals by changing **f** to **v** and adding **es**.

leaf ___   elf ___   shelf ___   wife ___   wolf __

Now for a mixture. Make all these words into plurals. Write out each complete word.

monkey ....   fly ....   shelf ....

pan ....   toy ....   fox ....

brush ....   loaf.................   bed ....

church................

97

RULE 35

MORE ABOUT PLURALS

These words do not follow the regular PLURAL rules, but they are such common words, that I have decided to
 include them here.

These words ending in **o**, add **es** when they become plurals.

volcano + es...........volcanoes

tomato + es.............tomatoes

potato + es.............potatoes

negro + es.............negroes

cargo + es.............cargoes

mosquito + es........mosquitoes

These words have irregular plurals

child - children   woman - women

foot - feet   tooth - teeth

goose - geese   man - men

ox - oxen   deer - deer

sheep - sheep   mouse - mice

MORE ABOUT PLURALS

Re-write these sentences in the plural. You may need to change the verb (action word) also. eg.   He is - They are.

1.   The child is playing here..

2.   The ox is in the field...

3.   Put the potato in the sack...

4.   I can hear a mosquito buzzing...

5.   The man walked very slowly...

6.   The sheep is bleating..

7.   The woman picked up a tomato...

8.   This little deer is lost...

9.   The negro sang as he worked..

10. This man is a hero..

11. The mouse ran to its hole...

12. My foot is hurting...

13. She had to have a tooth removed..

14. The farmer looked at his goose..

PART TWO

DIGRAPHS

LETTER PATTERNS

MNEMONICS

CONTENTS

PART TWO
DIGRAPHS, LETTER PATTERNS, MNEMONICS

ai	104
ay	106
air/are	108
ight	110
oo/ue/ew	112
oi/oy	114
o-e/oa/ow	116
ou/ow	118
er/ir/ur	120
or/aw/au	122
ee/ea/ie	124
cei	126
eer/ear/ere/ier	128
ear (er)	130
ough	132
el	134
Key words	136
Silent Letters	138
Mnemonics	140
Golden Key	142
Golden Key Word List	143
Index	144

This section deals mainly with some common letter patterns and digraphs. Letter patterns or digraphs, making the same sound, should initially be taught separately in order to avoid confusion. Worksheets containing several letter patterns, making the same sound are intended for revision only.

In Part Two, you will also find a number of mnemonics, rhymes and stories which will help to jog the memory.

I suggest that you colour each of the large letter patterns in one colour. Use this same colour to highlight, or underline these letters as they appear in the accompanying exercise. Use a different colour for each new letter pattern.

LETTER PATTERNS	A 'string' of vowel and consonants making one sound. eg **ough.**
DIGRAPHS	Two vowels making one sound. eg. **ai**
MNEMONICS	Memory aids.
KEY WORDS	High usage words, many of which have unusual spellings. eg. people

These two vowels make the long vowel sound **ā** in words.
NEVER use **ai** with Magic **e**.

You will see that most words in this group end with **ain** or **ail**.

rem**ai**n	s**ai**l	afr**ai**d	w**ai**t
p**ai**n	t**ai**l		
gr**ai**n	r**ai**l		
br**ai**n	p**ai**l		
ag**ai**n	m**ai**l		
dr**ai**n	h**ai**l		
Sp**ai**n	tr**ai**l		
ch**ai**n			
compl**ai**n			
p**ai**n			

ai

CLUES ACROSS

3. Stay still
6. A dog wags this
9. Once more
10. To grumble
13. You use this to think with
14. A country in Europe
16. A bucket
17. Rain water runs down this
18. A train runs on this

CLUES DOWN

1. Used on a boat to catch the wind
2. Comes from wheat
4. A snail leaves a silver one
5. Links connected together
7. Frozen rain
8. To stay
11. Frightened
12. The postman brings this
15. Fishermen put this on their lines
16. An ache

These letters also make the long vowel sound ā, but **ay** is nearly always seen at the end of words.

p**ay**	d**ay**	holid**ay**
s**ay**	st**ay**	m**ay**
yesterd**ay**	tod**ay**	pr**ay**
displ**ay**	tr**ay**	arr**ay**
Sund**ay**	Mond**ay**	Tuesd**ay**
Wednesd**ay**	Thursd**ay**	Frid**ay**
Saturd**ay**		

ay

Find the days of the week on this Wordsearch

M	S	A	T	U	R	D	A	Y	W
F	O	D	U	R	M	S	U	R	E
A	R	N	E	H	O	T	A	D	D
Y	F	I	S	U	N	D	A	Y	N
R	D	A	D	S	D	M	N	O	E
T	U	W	A	A	A	U	E	S	S
R	A	S	Y	E	Y	H	W	N	D
F	R	I	W	D	S	U	T	U	A
T	U	T	H	U	R	S	D	A	Y

Write the days of the week here.

The two letter patterns on this page make the same sound.

The following silly sentences may help you to remember some of the **air** words.

A h**air**y f**air**y in the d**air**y in desp**air**, going upst**air**s and downst**air**s looking for a p**air** of ch**air**s that needed a rep**air**.

desp**air**	p**air**
upst**air**s	ch**air**
air	f**air**
rep**air**	

You will find there are actually many **are** words that make the same sound as air. You will find these **are** words in the crossword.

W**are**	c**are**	welf**are**
h**are**	decl**are**	st**are**
prep**are**	sc**are**	gl**are**
m**are**	bew**are**	f**are**
sp**are**	sh**are**	r**are**

air/are

CLUES ACROSS

3. To be without hope
7. Two gloves, shoes etc.
8. To divide between
10. A seat
12. You go _____to bed
13. An extra one
15. Unusual, uncommon
16. You pay this to go on a bus
17. Be warned
19. To look hard at something
21. A female horse
22. We could not live without this

CLUES DOWN

1. A bright light
2. Blond
3. To announce
4. To mend
5. Help in the community
6. To get ready
9. Frighten
11. A large sort of rabbit
14. To look after
18. A town near Hertford
20. It grows on your head

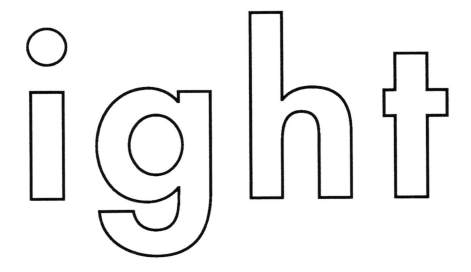

ight is a very common letter pattern which occurs in lots of words.

ight usually makes an ite sound. But watch out for the hidden **e** sound in the word height. In the words **e**ight and weight, you will hear an **ate** sound.

These sentences may help you to remember the spellings for **height** and **weight**.

He has great **he**ight.
We have great **we**ight.

You will find the following words in the crossword.

e**ight**	s**ight**
br**ight**	n**ight**
we**ight**	r**ight**
fl**ight**	he**ight**
f**ight**	l**ight**

ight

CLUES ACROSS
3. Clear and shining
5. Ability to fly
8. Opposite of left
10. Opposite of day

CLUES DOWN
1. Opposite of dark
2. Heaviness
4. Number after seven
6. To measure how high something is
7. Combat, battle
9. Ability to see

The letter patterns on this page make the same sound.

As heard in this sentence

It is **too** s**oo**n to go to sch**oo**l.

You will find some of the following words in the crossword.

sch**oo**l   br**oo**m   m**oo**n   st**oo**l   f**oo**d   gr**oo**m

sm**oo**th   s**oo**n

Learn these sentences. They contain many of the **ue** word.

    Don`t contin**ue** to arg**ue**.
    It is tr**ue** that S**ue** ate the bl**ue** gl**ue** on T**ue**sday.
    To the resc**ue** at the barbec**ue**.
    Give us a cl**ue**.

You will find some of the above **ue** words in the crossword.

Look for the **ew** words in this sentence.

She kn**ew** that the kite fl**ew** when the wind bl**ew**.

Here are some more **ew** words, some of which are in the crossword.

      st**ew**   n**ew**   gr**ew**   d**ew**   st**ew**

oo, ue, ew

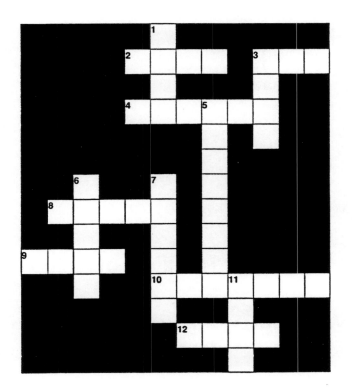

CLUES ACROSS

2. A colour
3. Not many
4. To save someone from danger
8. Used to sweep with
9. It shines in the sky at night
10. A day of the week
12. Jack's beanstalk......very tall

CLUES DOWN

1. A sticky substance
3. The birds _____ away
5. To carry on doing something
6. A person who looks after horses
7. Opposite of rough
11. A mixture of meat and vegetables

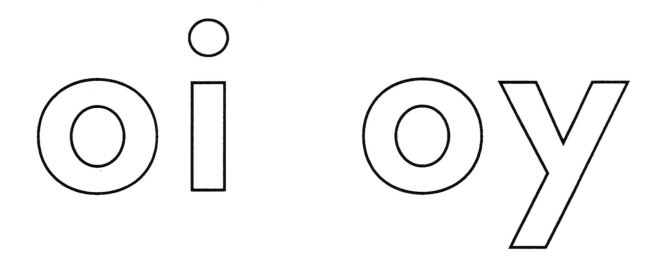

Both these digraphs make the same sound.

Learn this fun riddle. It is full of **oi** and **oy** words.

What n**oi**se ann**oy**s an **oy**ster most ?

A n**oi**sy n**oi**se ann**oy**s an **oy**ster most.

Here are a few more memory joggers.

Av**oi**d drinking p**oi**son.

R**oy**al people go for v**oy**ages in Rolls R**oy**ces and T**oy**otas.

B**oy**s enj**oy** t**oy**s.

B**oi**l the **oi**l.

The c**oi**n fell in the **oi**ntment.

Find all these words in the Wordsearch. Use two different colours - one for the **oi** words and one for the **oy** words.

OINTMENT POINT SOIL SPOIL COIN JOIN
VOICE NOISE ROYAL VOYAGE LOYAL OYSTER
BOY TOY ENJOY

S	P	O	I	L	C	O	I	N
S	J	O	Y	S	T	E	R	V
P	O	L	O	Y	A	L	V	O
O	I	N	T	M	E	N	T	Y
I	N	S	E	N	J	O	Y	A
N	C	Y	A	V	O	I	D	G
T	V	O	B	L	J	S	T	E
J	D	V	O	I	C	E	O	P
O	R	O	Y	A	L	C	Y	L

Here are four ways of making the long vowel sound of o.

Magic **e** makes the vowel sound say its name.

bone home note alone hope smoke joke spoke

NEVER use this digraph with Magic **e**. You will not find **oa** at the end of words. **oa** is seen in the following sentences

The g**oa**t had a c**oa**t stuck in its thr**oa**t.
A t**oa**d in the r**oa**d.
She m**oa**ns and gr**oa**ns.
Put the t**oa**st in the t**oa**ster.

This digraph is usually found at the end of words.

gr**ow**	arr**ow**	yell**ow**
sh**ow**	marr**ow**	pill**ow**
kn**ow**	narr**ow**	holl**ow**
bl**ow**	barr**ow**	foll**ow**
gl**ow**	sparr**ow**	will**ow**

Sometimes in short words, letter o says its own name.

old m**o**st b**o**th **o**nly s**o**ld h**o**st

116

ANSWER ALL THE CLUES WITH AN
oa, **o - e**, **ow**, or **o** WORD

A dog likes to eat one ....

Water round a castle ....

Opposite of young ....

In winter it is often ....

To get bigger..

A farm animal with a beard ....

We rest our head on this when we go to sleep ....

A primary colour ....

A garment to keep you warm ....

To recognise or be acquainted ....

A footballer hopes to score this ....

These let light into a house ....

A tree with drooping branches ....

A large type of frog ....

To get bigger ....

A garment to keep you warm ....

To recognise or be acquainted with ....

The day after today ....

OU OW

These two letter pairs make the same sound.

OU

These sentences will help you to remember the **ou** words

I **fou**nd a p**ou**nd on the gr**ou**nd.
Look **ou**t, look **ou**t. There`s a m**ou**se in the h**ou**se.
Out and ab**ou**t.

OW

These sentences will help you to remember the **ow** words.

She went d**ow**n to t**ow**n in a br**ow**n g**ow**n.
Spring sh**ow**ers bring summer fl**ow**ers.
Fl**ow**er p**ow**er.
The king wears a fr**ow**n and a golden cr**ow**n.

OU OW

H	O	U	S	E	F	O	T	B
C	O	U	N	T	O	S	W	R
A	M	F	M	O	U	S	E	O
D	U	L	O	W	N	C	O	W
S	M	O	U	N	T	A	I	N
H	O	W	L	I	A	S	L	M
O	U	E	O	S	I	N	O	W
U	S	R	W	U	N	P	U	E
T	E	R	P	O	W	E	R	N

Can you find all these words in the Wordsearch ?

MOUSE FOUNTAIN HOUSE OUR MOUNTAIN COUNT
SHOUT BROWN FLOWER COW TOWN HOW POWER
NOW

er ir ur

These letter pairs have the same sound.

er is usually found at the end of words. You will find these words in the crossword.

butter father slower robber farmer driver another

ir is found in the following phrases.

Thirty dirty shirts.
Thirsty girls first.
A bird in a fir tree.
Girls in skirts.

You will find these **ir** words in the crossword.

skirt thirty thirteen third bird thirsty

This little story will help you to remember many of the **ur** words.

The burglar goes out each Thursday. He gets hurt. He gets burnt, and his face turns purple. He needs a nurse.He runs behind the church and gets frightened by a turkey. He returns home on Saturday without his purse.

You will find these words in the crossword.

Saturday burn Thursday return nurse church nurse purple

er ir ur

CLUES ACROSS

2. Worn by a boy
5. This is spread on bread
6. Worn by a girl
7. Two days before Monday
9. Greater
15. A fire does this
16. Number after twelve
18. Male parent
19. Less quick
20. One who steals
22. One who works the land
23. Person at the wheel of a car

CLUES DOWN

1. Number after twenty nine
3. Needing a drink
4. First, second _____
8. Day after Wednesday
10. To go back
11. Works in a hospital
12. A place to keep money
13. A place of worship
14. One more
17. Mix red and blue
21 An animal which flies

or aw au

These letter pairs all make the same sound.

You will find **or** in many words. Look out for these words in the crossword.

stor**y** m**or**ning platf**or**m exp**or**ts **or**chestra t**or**ch

You will find lots of **aw** words in this story. Make a sketch to help you to remember the words.

I s**aw** her on the l**aw**n at d**aw**n. She gave a y**aw**n, and broke her j**aw**. She had to cr**aw**l back to the str**aw**. It was **aw**ful.

Look out for these words in the crossword.

cr**aw**l s**aw** dr**aw** y**aw**n cl**aw**s l**aw**n **aw**ful l**aw**

Find the **au** words in these sentences.

The **au**thor drove off in his **au**tomatic car.
When **Au**gust is over, it will soon be **Au**tumn.
S**au**sages and s**au**ce on a s**au**cer.

You will find these words in the crossword.

s**au**cer s**au**ce **Au**gust **au**tomatic h**au**nted s**au**sages f**au**lt **au**tumn

122

or aw au

CLUES ACROSS

1. Very early in the morning
2. A tale
4. A cup rests on this
6. Time of day before noon
9. A machine working on its own
12. A house with ghosts
13. Eaten with beans and chips
14. Something to pour on chips
17. You wait here for the train
19. If you are to blame, it is
    your _____
20. A baby does this
22. A summer month
23. To have seen

CLUES DOWN

1. You do this with a pen or pencil
3. When you are tired you do this
5. Goods sent out of the country
7. A group of musicians
8. People watching a concert
10. A season
11. Animals have sharp ones
15. Dreadful
16. A light held in the hand
18. An area of short grass
21. Break this, and you go to prison

The three letter pairs on this page all make the same sound.

This letter pair is seen in the following sentences.

I s**ee** a b**ee** in a tr**ee**.
Every w**ee**k play hide and s**ee**k.
F**ee**t m**ee**t in the str**ee**t.

This is the **eating** sound as seen in these 'food' words.

t**ea** b**ea**ns p**ea**s m**ea**t cr**ea**m p**ea**ches

You will also find lots of 'each' words here

The t**ea**cher t**ea**ches **ea**ch of us to r**ea**d.

There is another way of making this sound

There are not many words with this pattern. You will remember the order of the letters if you think of **ie** as in p**ie**. Then say A p**ie**ce of p**ie**.

ie

Highlight the **ie** words in this story. Make a sketch to help you to remember the words.

It's my bel**ie**f that the n**ie**ce of the ch**ie**f th**ie**f stole a p**ie**ce of the handkerch**ie**f, and hid it in the f**ie**ld by the sh**ie**ld.

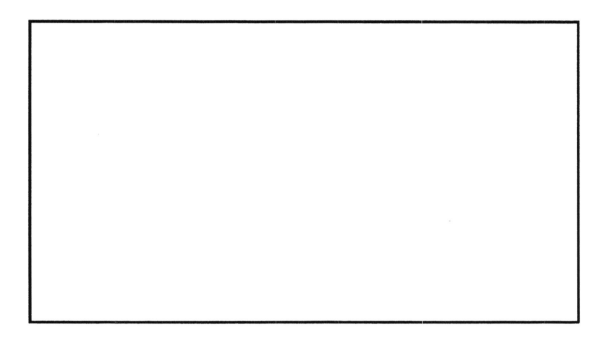

Write out all the **ie** words from the story.

cei

You may have heard a very famous spelling rule which says

i before **e**, except after **c**.

The four commonest words, which follow this rule are these.

1. re**cei**ve - re**cei**ving re**cei**ved

2. de**cei**ve - de**cei**ving de**cei**ved

3. con**cei**t - con**cei**ted

4. **cei**ling

cei

Colour in the **cei** parts of these words.

re c e i ve

de c e i ve

con c e i ted

c e i ling

Now make a sentence for each of these four words

1. ....

2. ....

3. ....

4. ....

eer ear ere ier

All these letter patterns make the same sound. Make each one a different colour. Use each of these colours to highlight the letter patterns in the words below.

eer

volunt**eer**	domin**eer**	pion**eer**
ch**eer**	j**eer**	st**eer**
d**eer**	engin**eer**	b**eer**

ear

f**ear**	d**ear**	cl**ear**
n**ear**	n**ear**ly	y**ear**
h**ear**	dr**ear**y	w**ear**y

ere

h**ere**	interf**ere**	sinc**ere**
sev**ere**	atmosph**ere**	persev**ere**

ier

chandel**ier**	grenad**ier**	p**ier**
cash**ier**	gondol**ier**	p**ier**ce

ANSWER ALL THESE CLUES WITH AN
eer, ear, ere, or **ier** WORD

A loud applause ....eer

Bright ....ear

An ornamental support for candles ....ier

A guardsman ....ier

A drink made from malt ....eer

To guide by mechanical means ....eer

Harsh, strict ....ere

A wild animal with antlers ....eer

We do this with our ears ....ear

To meddle ....ere

Twelve months ....ear

Not far away ....ear

One who sails a gondola ....ier

One who looks after cash ....ier

Genuine ....ere

ear saying er

In a few important words the letter pattern **ear** can sound like **er**.

s **e a r** ch   res **e a r** ch

h **ear** d   l **ear** n

l **e a r** ned   p **e a r** l

e a r th   **e a r** ly

e a r liest   **e a r** l

ear saying er

Learn this sentence containing lots of **ear** words which sound like **er**. Make a sketch to help you to remember them.

I s**ear**ched **ear**ly in the **ear**th for the p**ear**l, and l**ear**ned I had **ear**ned a reward.

ough

This is probably the most confusing letter pattern in our written language. **ough** in fact represents seven different sounds.

ough sounds like **uff** in r**ough** t**ough** en**ough**

ough sounds like **off** in c**ough**, tr**ough**

ough sounds like **o** (so) in d**ough** th**ough** alth**ough**

ough sounds like **ow** (cow) in b**ough** pl**ough**

ough sounds like **oo** in thr**ough**

Add a **t** to **ough**, and **ought** sounds like **ort** in

ought th**ought** f**ought** b**ought** br**ought** n**ought** s**ought**

ought sounds like **out** in dr**ought**

132

ough

CLUES ACROSS
3. Zero
5. An idea
7. Have you br_____ your things ?
9. Sufficient
10. Bread mixture
12. Used by farmers
13. Obliged to
14. Branch of a tree

CLUES DOWN
1. Had a fight
2. Even if
4. Not smooth
6. We walked thr___the wood
8. A noise made in the throat
11. Hardy, strong

e‍l AT THE END OF A WORD

Although the **le** rule (see Rule 19) usually applies, there are a few important exceptions which end in **el**.

Amongst the most common, are the following

tow**el**	flann**el**	trav**el**
tunn**el**	pan**el**	mod**el**
chann**el**		

TEACHER`S NOTE

You should also draw attention to the few **al** endings like metal pedal medal

e**l** AT THE END OF A WORD

Make sketches to help you to remember these **el** words.

Ellie took a flann**el** and a tow**el** to trav**el** through the chann**el** tunn**el**

The pan**el** of judges gave first prize to the mod**el** made of enam**el**.

KEY WORDS

Key words are those words which we all use a great deal in writing, but which do not always follow regular spelling rules. The spelling of these words is often quite difficult. You can learn to spell over a hundred of these words in an easy and enjoyable way by using the two volumes of **The Golden Key, Spelling by Singing** series (with Audio tape)

In the crossword, you will find the following Key words

talk	every	after
once	house	laugh
before	school	noise
shout	where	believe
please	little	station
quiet	mother	baby
beautiful	before	walk
write		

KEY WORDS

CLUES ACROSS

3. To speak in a loud voice
4. You say this, if you want something
6. Small
7. Another word for Mummy
10. Lovely
12. To stroll along
13. You do this with a pencil or pen
15. To do as one is told
16. A place of learning
17. Where people live
19. They lived happily ever ......

CLUES DOWN

1. ..... are you going?
2. To accept what someone says
5. You catch a train here
6. Silent
9. A tiny child
10. Opposite of after
11. Ha ha ha
14. A loud sound
18. ..... upon a time
20. To speak to someone

SOME SILENT LETTERS

Silent w

wring write wrote writing wrist wriggle wrong wrap

Silent k

kneel kneeling knelt knife knickers knight knuckles knob
know knew knowledge knock

Silent g

gnarled gnome gnaw foreign reign campaign

Silent u

disguise guitar guess guest guilty guard guide

SOME SILENT LETTERS

Highlight the silent letters, and make sketches to illustrate each sentence.

Wring your wrists

Kneel on your knees

The knight had a knife
in his knitted knickers

The reigning king joined
the foreign campaign

The gnarled old gnome
gnawed the toadstool

Guess who is in disguise
and playing a guitar

MNEMONICS

Mnemonics is a word which simply means "memory jogger."
If you take the first letter from each word in the following
sentences, the letters will make a word which has a difficult
spelling. You may recognise some of the well known ones.

because
big **e**lephants **c**an`t **a**lways **u**se **s**mall **e**ntrances.

laugh
lions **a**nd **u**nicorns **g**o **h**a ha ha.

school
Sammy **c**ame **h**ome **o**n **O**scar`s **l**orry

neighbour
not **e**very **i**ndividual **g**oes **h**ome **b**y **o**ld **u**nderground **r**ailway

necessary
never **e**at **c**ake, **e**at **s**alad **s**andwiches **a**nd **r**emain **y**oung

difficulty
Mrs **d** Mrs **i** Mrs **ffi** Mrs **c**   Mrs **u** Mrs **lty**

arithmetic
a red indian thinks he may eat toffee in church

field
four indian elephants lie down

Now here are a few different sorts of memory joggers.

island
an **island** is **land** surrounded by water.

busy
The **busy bus** carries **busy** people.

friend
I will be your friend to the **end**.

young

You are **you**ng

money

o - n - e that spells one.
Now the fun has just begun.
With m in front, and y at the end.
You'll have **money**, yes my friend.
With your **money**, what will you buy ?
Money, money, money, m - o - n - e - y

THE GOLDEN KEY
Spelling by Singing

You may be interested to hear about the Golden Key books written by Joan Walton. Together the books make up a collection of tuneful songs which aim to cover the spellings of over a hundred of our most commonly used words. Each book has an accompanying audio cassette tape, which contains all the songs in the book. The songs which are sung by a group of children are recorded on both sides of the tape.

The Golden Key books are attractively presented and each contains fun worksheets to reinforce the words which have been learned. The suggested age range is 5 - 9 years.

There are two versions of these books, and the words covered are shown on the opposite page.

Children`s Version
Contains 23 worksheets, non photocopiable, Price £5.99 each
Vol. 1 with Audio Tape ISBN 1-674757-04-6
Vol. 2 with Audio tape ISBN 1-874757-05-4

Teacher`s Version contains original music
Spiral bound with photocopiable worksheets Price £12.50
Vol 1. with Audio tape ISBN 1-874757-00-3
Vol 2. with Audio tape ISBN 1-874757-02-X

OVER A HUNDRED HIGH USAGE WORDS TO LEARN BY SINGING

GOLDEN KEY WORDS

VOLUME 1	VOLUME 2
beautiful	busy
would, could	every
any, many	please
one, two	aught words
question words	cian words
ough words	words ending in e
because	only
ight words	success
laugh	water
pretty	other
said	write
tion words	noise, noisy
autumn	believe
some, come	money
baby	little
people	ound words
does, goes	house, mouse
school	listen
ey words	out words
friend	ology words
once	before, more
walk, talk	quiet
with	after

INDEX

A

able 28, 29, 58, 59, 86, 87
ai 104, 105
air 108, 109
al/all 64, 65
alphabet 8, 9
ance 16, 17, 88, 89
are 108, 109
au 122,123
aw 122, 123
ay 78, 79, 96, 97, 104, 105

B

blends 4

C

hard c 40, 41
soft c 28, 29, 58, 59, 82-85
cei 126, 127
changing 'y' to 'i' 62,63, 58, 59,
76, 77, 96, 97
cial 70, 71
cian 70, 71
cious 70, 71
ck 34, 35
consonants 8, 9, 30, 31

D

dge 50, 51
digraphs 4, 103
doubling 18, 19, 46, 47, 54, 55
dropping e 26-29, 58,59

E

magic 'e' 22-29
dropping e 26-29, 58, 59
keeping e 58, 59, 86-89
ea 124
ear 128, 129
ear (er) 130, 131
ee 124
eer 128, 129
el 134, 135
ence 88, 89
er 120, 121
ere 128, 129
ew 112, 113
ey 78, 79, 96, 97

F

flossy words (ff, ll, ss) 46, 47
ful/full 30, 31, 64, 65

G

hard 'g' 40, 41
soft 'g' 28, 29, 82-87

I

ic 42, 43
ie (final) 24, 25
ie (medial) 124, 125
ier 128, 129
ight 110,111
ing 26,76, 77
ir 120, 121

J

j 84, 85

K

k or c (initial) 40, 41
k (final) 36, 37
ke 34, 35
key words 3, 4, 136, 137
kn 138, 139

L

le 54-59
less 30, 31
lk 36, 37
ly 30, 31 62, 63

M

magic e 22-29
ment 30, 31
mnemonics 4, 103, 140, 141

N

ness 30, 31
nk 36, 37

O

oa 116, 117
o-e 116, 117
oi 114,115
oo 112,113
or 122,123
ou 118,119
ough 132, 133
ow(cow) 118, 119

ow(low) 116, 117
oy 78, 79, 94, 114, 115

P

plurals 96,97
prefixes 16, 17

R

roots 16, 17

S

short vowel endings 34-37, 46-51
silent letters 138, 139
sion 68, 69
ssion 68
stle 56, 57
suffixing 26-32, 34, 54, 55, 58, 59, 62-65, 68-71, 76-79, 86-89, 96, 97
syllables 12, 13, 42, 43, 96, 97

T

tial 70
tient 70
til/till 64,65
tion 68, 69
tious 70

U

ue 24, 25, 112, 113
ur 120,121

V

vowels (short) 10, 11, 18, 19, 22, 23, 34-37, 46-47, 50, 51, 54, 55
vowels (long) 10, 11, 22, 23, 34, 35, 54, 55,68, 69

W

w rules 91, 92
wr 138, 139

Y

y (final) 74-79, 62, 63, 96
y to i 58, 59, 62, 63, 76, 77, 96, 97